3800 12 0079840 7

D0509978

Jack and the Beanstalk

WRITTEN BY

VIVIAN FRENCH

ILLUSTRATED BY

HARRY HORSE

WALKER BOOKS
AND SUBSIDIARIES

LONDON • BOSTON • SYDNEY • AU

HIGH LIFE HIGHLAND	
3800 12 0079840 7	
Askews & Holts	Nov-2012
822.914	£4.99

WITHDRAWN

First published 2001 by Walker Books Ltd, 87 Vauxhall Walk, London SE11 5HJ

This edition published 2012

2 4 6 8 10 9 7 5 3 1

Text © 2001 Vivian French
Illustrations © 2001 Harry Horse

The right of Vivian French and Harry Horse to be identified as
author and illustrator respectively of this work has been asserted by them
in accordance with the Copyright, Designs and Patents Act 1988

This book has been typeset in Goudy

Printed in China

All rights reserved. No part of this book may be reproduced, transmitted
or stored in an information retrieval system in any form or by any means, graphic,
electronic or mechanical, including photocopying, taping and recording,
without prior written permission from the publisher.

British Library Cataloguing in Publication Data:
a catalogue record for this book is available from the British Library

ISBN 978-1-4063-4338-0

www.walker.co.uk

Notes for Children

Jack and the Beanstalk is the story of a
poor boy and a greedy giant.
You may know the story already, but it doesn't
matter if you don't.

This book is a little different from other picture books.
You will be sharing it with other people and telling
the story together.

You can read

this line

this line

this line

or this line.

Even when someone else is reading, try to follow
the words. It will help when it's your turn!

FEE! FI! FO! FUM!

FEE! FI! FO! FUM!

This is a story

About a boy.

What was his name?

His name was Jack.

FEE! FI! FO! FUM!

FEE! FI! FO! FUM!

Jack was poor

And his mum was poor.

Why were they poor?

When Jack was little

A giant came.

He stole their gold –

Clink! Clink!

Clink! Clink! Clink!

He stole their hen

A magic hen –

Cluck! Cluck!

Cluck! Cluck! Cluck!

He stole their harp

A magic harp –

Plink! Plink!

Plink! Plink! Plink!

So Jack was poor

And his mum was poor

And they both got poorer

Poorer and poorer.

Nothing for breakfast.

Nothing for dinner.

Nothing for tea.

Nothing at all.

So Jack's mum said,

"Jack, sell the cow –"

Moo! Moo!

Moo! Moo! Moo!

"Take her to market,

Quickly now!"

Moo! Moo!

Moo! Moo! Moo!

Jack and the cow

Went down the road

And then they met

A little old man.

And the little old man

Bought the cow

For five beans –

Magic beans.

But Jack's mum said,

"You silly boy!"

She took the beans –

The magic beans –

And threw them away!

But in the night

A beanstalk grew

Up and up –

Wizz! Wizz!

Wizz! Wizz! Wizz!

And Jack climbed up.

Up to the top?

The very top.

He went to the house

The giant's house –

Knock! Knock!

Knock! Knock! Knock!

The giant's wife said,

"Do come in!"

And Jack went in

And there he saw

The bags of gold

The hen and the harp –

Clink! Clink!

Cluck! Cluck! Plink!

The giant came

The big big giant.

Jack hid away.

The giant sniffed

And sniffed and sniffed.

"I SMELL A BOY!

FEE! FI! FO! FUM!

FEE! FI! FO! FUM!"

But he couldn't find Jack

He couldn't find Jack

He couldn't find Jack at all.

The giant's wife said,

"Eat your dinner!"

And the giant ate –

YUM! YUM!

YUM! YUM! YUM!

When the giant was sleeping –

SNORE! SNORE!

SNORE! SNORE! SNORE!

Jack came creeping.

He took the gold –

Clink! Clink!

Clink! Clink! Clink!

He took the gold

Back to his mother.

He slid down the beanstalk –

WHEEEEEEEEEE!

WHEEEEEEEEEEE!

All the way down

Down the beanstalk.

What came next?

Jack went back

Back up the beanstalk

Up to the top.

He went to the house

The giant's house –

Knock! Knock!

Knock! Knock! Knock!

The giant's wife said,

"Do come in!"

And Jack went in

And there he saw

The hen and the harp!

Cluck! Cluck!

Plink! Plink! Plink!

The giant came

The big big giant.

And the giant sniffed

And sniffed and sniffed.

"I SMELL A BOY!

FEE! FI! FO! FUM!

FEE! FI! FO! FUM!"

But he couldn't find Jack

He couldn't find Jack

He couldn't find Jack at all.

The giant's wife said,

"Eat your dinner!"

And the giant ate –

YUM! YUM!

YUM! YUM! YUM!

When the giant was sleeping –

SNORE! SNORE!

SNORE! SNORE! SNORE!

Jack came creeping.

He took the hen –

Cluck! Cluck!

Cluck! Cluck! Cluck!

He took the hen

Back to his mother.

He slid down the beanstalk –

WHEEEEEEEEEEE!

WHEEEEEEEEEEEE!

All the way down

Down the beanstalk.

What came next?

Jack went back

Back up the beanstalk

Back to the house

The giant's house.

When the giant was sleeping

Jack came creeping.

He took the harp

Back to his mother.

But the giant woke up!

"I SMELL A BOY!

I SEE A BOY!"

The giant chased Jack.

Jack slid down the beanstalk –

WHEEEEEEEEEEE!

But the giant came too –

WHOOOOOOOOOOOSH!

Then Jack called out,

"Mum! Fetch an axe!

Quick! Quick!

Fetch an axe!"

He cut down the beanstalk –

CRASH!

And the giant fell down –

CRASH!!

And that was the end of the giant.

And that was the end of the story.

And Jack and his mum

Lived happily ever after.

FEE! FI! FO! FUM!

Jack is happy with his mum!

Notes for Teachers

Story Plays are written and presented in a way that encourages children to read aloud together. They are dramatic versions of memorable and exciting stories, told in strongly patterned language which gives children the chance to practise at a vital stage of their reading development. Sharing stories in this way makes reading an active and enjoyable process, and one that draws in even the reticent reader.

The story is told by four different voices, divided into four colours so that each child can easily read his or her part. The blue line is for more experienced readers; the red line for less experienced readers. When there are more than four children in a group, there is an ideal opportunity for paired reading. Partnering a more experienced reader with a less experienced one can be very supportive and provides a learning experience for both children.

Story Plays encourage children to share in the reading of a whole text in a collaborative and interactive way. This makes them perfect for group and guided reading activities. Children will find they need to pay close attention to the print and punctuation, and to use the meaning of the whole story in order to read it with expression and a real sense of voice.